Think → Write → Share

TAGAKI®

Advanced 2

Around the World

Search for information on 30 countries
Write three good points about each topic

In TAGAKI Advanced 2 the user searches for information on 30 countries presented in alphabetical order. The aim is to entice users to take an interest in all countries of the world—including their nature, history, and culture—and to respect the people who live there.

The focus is on finding good things about each topic—looking up positive aspects that the people of that country would be proud of and reporting them in an optimistic way.

In the globalized world, you never know where and when you will meet people from elsewhere. The hope behind this workbook is that users increase their ability to create positive relationships and have respect for everyone as a fellow human being.

TAGAKI Advanced 2

Around the World

Contents

1 Reading and Listening Time

Read the sample sentences written about chosen topic.
Listen to the audio.

1 Adventures

Please note that the audio recording of this book contains pronunciations of some words as commonly spoken by users of American English.

Sample Sentences

Country
Angola

Useful Expressions
Use some of the useful expressions, if you like.

 If you dream of having African adventures, Angola is the place for you!

Body ❶ Enjoy abundant wildlife and the African savanna in the Kissama National Park, which has safaris, rivers and distinctive trees. The park is almost as big as Osaka and Hyogo prefectures combined!

❷ One of the country's most famous spots is Kalandula Falls. It is extremely thrilling to view the panorama from the top of the falls.

❸ Tundavala is a natural viewpoint 2,200 meters above sea level. There is no doubt you will be amazed by the mountainous formations you can see!

Closing Be careful! Do not fall off while standing on top of Kalandula Falls.

 If I Go There

Angola is the place to have the adventure of a lifetime. I really love animals, so taking a safari in the jungles of Angola would be a dream come true.

How to write your own version

Countries Choose one country, research it, mark it on the world map, and draw its national flag.

Opening Write at least one sentence as an introduction.

Body Make use of what you researched and write three good points about the topic.

Closing Write at least one sentence as a closing.

 If I Go There
Write what you want to experience in the country if you could go there.

Choose one country you'd like to research from the box (except the one used in the sample sentences).

Using the structure of the sample sentences, write more than 100 words.
Use some of the useful expressions, if you like.

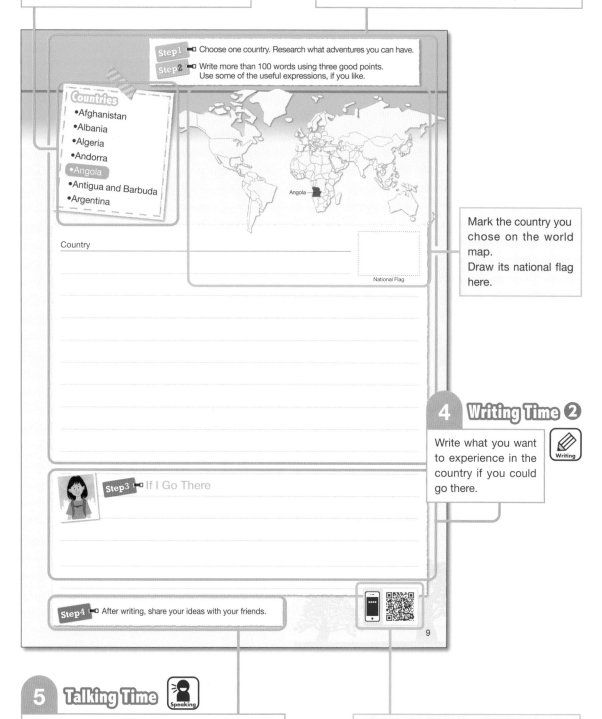

Step1 ▪️▫️ Choose one country. Research what adventures you can have.

Step2 ▪️▫️ Write more than 100 words using three good points.
Use some of the useful expressions, if you like.

Countries
- Afghanistan
- Albania
- Algeria
- Andorra
- Angola
- Antigua and Barbuda
- Argentina

Angola

Country _____

National Flag

Mark the country you chose on the world map.
Draw its national flag here.

Step3 ▪️▫️ If I Go There

Write what you want to experience in the country if you could go there.

Step4 ▪️▫️ After writing, share your ideas with your friends.

9

Present what you wrote by reading it out loud, or even better, memorize it, then present it.

Listen to the sample sentences
the way they are spoken with contractions.

World Map

28 Turkey
4 Bosnia and Herzegovina
10 Georgia
18 Mongolia
20 Norway
21 Poland
2 Austria
15 Liechtenstein
26 Switzerland
13 Italy
9 Egypt
14 Jordan
12 India
27 Thailand
5 Cambodia
22 Republic of Kor (South Korea)
11 Ghana
29 United Republic of Tanzania (Tanzania)
24 Singapore
1 Angola
16 Madagascar
19 Namibia
30 Zimbabwe
25 South Africa

Afghanistan
Albania
Algeria
Andorra
Angola ❶
Antigua and Barbuda
Argentina
Armenia
Australia
Austria ❷
Azerbaijan
Bahamas
Bahrain
Bangladesh
Barbados
Belarus
Belgium
Belize ❸
Benin
Bhutan
Bolivarian Republic of Venezuela (Venezuela)
Bosnia and Herzegovina ❹
Botswana
Brazil
Brunei Darussalam (Brunei)

Bulgaria
Burkina Faso
Burundi
Cambodia ❺
Cameroon
Canada
Cape Verde
Central African Republic
Chad
Chile ❻
China
Colombia
Comoros
Congo
Costa Rica ❼
Croatia
Cuba
Cyprus
Czech Republic
Democratic People's Republic of Korea (North Korea)
Democratic Republic of the Congo
Denmark
Djibouti
Dominica
Dominican Republic ❽
Ecuador

Egypt ❾
El Salvador
Equatorial Guinea
Eritrea
Estonia
Eswatini
Ethiopia
Federated States of Micronesia (Micronesia)
Fiji
Finland
France
Gabon
Georgia ❿
Germany
Ghana ⓫
Greece
Grenada
Guatemala
Guinea
Guinea-Bissau
Guyana
Haiti
Honduras
Hungary
Iceland
India ⓬

Indonesia
Iraq
Ireland
Islamic Republic of Iran (Iran)
Israel
Italy ⓭
Ivory Coast
Jamaica
Japan
Jordan ⓮
Kazakhstan
Kenya
Kiribati
Kuwait
Kyrgyzstan
Lao People's Democratic Republic (Laos)
Latvia
Lebanon
Lesotho
Liberia
Libya
Liechtenstein ⓯
Lithuania
Luxembourg
Madagascar ⓰

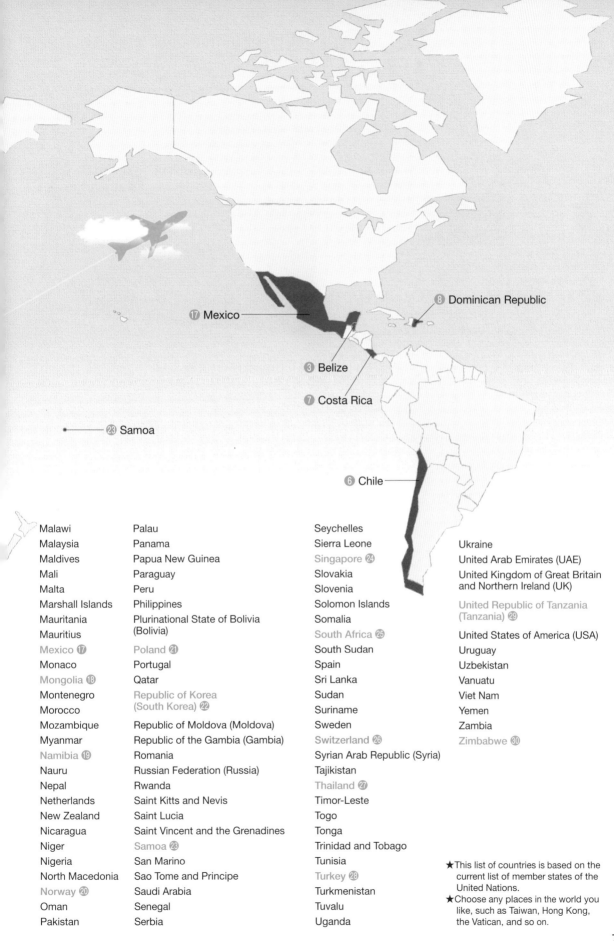

⑧ Dominican Republic

⑰ Mexico

③ Belize

⑦ Costa Rica

㉓ Samoa

⑥ Chile

Malawi	Palau	Seychelles	
Malaysia	Panama	Sierra Leone	Ukraine
Maldives	Papua New Guinea	Singapore ㉔	United Arab Emirates (UAE)
Mali	Paraguay	Slovakia	United Kingdom of Great Britain
Malta	Peru	Slovenia	and Northern Ireland (UK)
Marshall Islands	Philippines	Solomon Islands	United Republic of Tanzania
Mauritania	Plurinational State of Bolivia	Somalia	(Tanzania) ㉙
Mauritius	(Bolivia)	South Africa ㉕	United States of America (USA)
Mexico ⑰	Poland ㉑	South Sudan	Uruguay
Monaco	Portugal	Spain	Uzbekistan
Mongolia ⑱	Qatar	Sri Lanka	Vanuatu
Montenegro	Republic of Korea	Sudan	Viet Nam
Morocco	(South Korea) ㉒	Suriname	Yemen
Mozambique	Republic of Moldova (Moldova)	Sweden	Zambia
Myanmar	Republic of the Gambia (Gambia)	Switzerland ㉖	Zimbabwe ㉚
Namibia ⑲	Romania	Syrian Arab Republic (Syria)	
Nauru	Russian Federation (Russia)	Tajikistan	
Nepal	Rwanda	Thailand ㉗	
Netherlands	Saint Kitts and Nevis	Timor-Leste	
New Zealand	Saint Lucia	Togo	
Nicaragua	Saint Vincent and the Grenadines	Tonga	
Niger	Samoa ㉓	Trinidad and Tobago	
Nigeria	San Marino	Tunisia	
North Macedonia	Sao Tome and Principe	Turkey ㉘	
Norway ⑳	Saudi Arabia	Turkmenistan	
Oman	Senegal	Tuvalu	
Pakistan	Serbia	Uganda	

★This list of countries is based on the
current list of member states of the
United Nations.
★Choose any places in the world you
like, such as Taiwan, Hong Kong,
the Vatican, and so on.

1 Adventures

Country
Angola

Opening If you dream of having African adventures, Angola is the place for you!

Body ❶ Enjoy abundant <u>wildlife</u> and the African savanna in the Kissama National Park, which has safaris, rivers and distinctive trees. The park is almost as big as Osaka and Hyogo prefectures combined!

❷ One of the country's <u>most famous spots</u> is Kalandula Falls. It is <u>extremely thrilling to</u> view the panorama from the top of the falls.

❸ Tundavala is a natural viewpoint 2,200 meters above sea level. <u>There is no doubt</u> you will be amazed by the mountainous formations you can see!

Closing Be careful! Do not fall off while standing on top of Kalandula Falls.

 If I Go There

Angola is the place to have the adventure of a lifetime. I really love animals, so taking a safari in the jungles of Angola would be a dream come true.

Step1 ▪◻ Choose one country. Research what adventures you can have.

Step2 ▪◻ Write more than 100 words using three good points.
Use some of the useful expressions, if you like.

Countries

- Afghanistan
- Albania
- Algeria
- Andorra
- Angola
- Antigua and Barbuda
- Argentina

Angola

Country _____

National Flag

Step3 ▪◻ If I Go There

Step4 ▪◻ After writing, share your ideas with your friends.

Country
Austria

| Opening | The birthplace of Mozart and Strauss is also home to magnificent architecture. |

| Body | ① The Hofburg Palace is the beautiful official residence of the President of Austria.
② Additionally, the Vienna State Opera House is a very popular tourist spot and has been the location of great artistic performances since 1869.
③ The Gasometers in Vienna are four converted gas tanks now used as apartments, offices and shops. They are perfect examples of how old structures can be renovated and transformed for modern use. |

| Closing | Rain or shine, hot or cold, it is a great idea to walk around this beautiful city to view an amazing variety of inspiring and innovative structures. |

If I Go There

I would like to attend a classical music concert at the Vienna State Opera House and afterward have coffee and Austrian pastry in a nice cafe. That would make a great memory.

Step1 ▶ Choose one country. Research what kind of architecture they have.

Step2 ▶ Write more than 100 words using three good points. Use some of the useful expressions, if you like.

Countries
- Armenia
- Australia
- Austria
- Azerbaijan
- Bahamas ※
- Bahrain

Austria

※Please use "the" before this country name if you use it in a sentence.

Country _____

....

National Flag

Step3 ▶ If I Go There

Step4 ▶ After writing, share your ideas with your friends.

3 Birds

Country

Belize

Opening For such a tiny nation, Belize has a really gorgeous national bird.

Body
1. The keel-billed toucan is one of the world's most famous birds due to its unique appearance.
2. They have black bodies with bright yellow chest feathers and are most well known for their large curved bills which make them really stand out. An average bill is about 12-15 centimeters in length.
3. The keel-billed toucan was designated the national bird because it is instantly recognizable and found throughout the forests of Belize.

Closing The country is a bird watcher's paradise! Take a trip there to see as many of our feathered friends as you can.

If I Go There

Visiting the Hol Chan Marine Reserve would be incredible snorkeling fun! It is vast and separated into many sections. I am sure I would see lots of interesting sea life.

Step 1 ◻ Choose one country. Research what birds they have.

Step 2 ◻ Write more than 100 words using three good points.
Use some of the useful expressions, if you like.

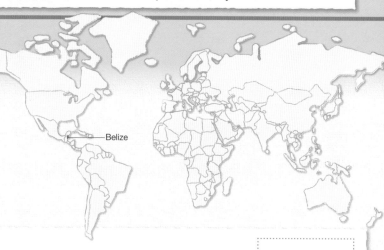

Countries
- Bangladesh
- Barbados
- Belarus
- Belgium
- Belize
- Benin
- Bhutan

Belize

Country _____

National Flag

Step 3 ◻ If I Go There

Step 4 ◻ After writing, share your ideas with your friends.

Country
Bosnia and Herzegovina

Opening The Bosnian capital of Sarajevo, which hosted the 1984 Winter Olympics, is a city that has risen from the aftermath of conflicts time and time again!

Body
① In my personal opinion, Bascarsija is Sarajevo's historical and cultural center. The beautiful old-style market area was built in the 15th century and is a major tourist attraction.

② The National Library (Vijecnica) was beautifully restored in 2014 and is the symbol of the city.

③ Playing chess in the many city parks is a very popular pastime for its citizens.

Closing Reconstruction of the capital is almost completed and today Sarajevo is again one of the most beautiful cities in Europe.

If I Go There

I would like to see the Stari Most Bridge. This iconic landmark was constructed in the mid-16th century, destroyed during the Bosnian War, and rebuilt in 2004. I think it truly represents the spirit of the Bosnian people.

Step 1 ➟ Choose one country. Research what the capital city is like.

Step 2 ➟ Write more than 100 words using three good points.
Use some of the useful expressions, if you like.

Countries

- Bolivarian Republic of Venezuela (Venezuela)
- Bosnia and Herzegovina
- Botswana
- Brazil
- Brunei Darussalam (Brunei)
- Bulgaria

Bosnia and Herzegovina

Country _____

National Flag

Step 3 ➟ If I Go There

Step 4 ➟ After writing, share your ideas with your friends.

5 Celebrities

Country
Cambodia

Opening A celebrity does not have to be a sports star or a performer. In Cambodia, a man became famous for making his country safer.

Body
❶ Aki Ra was a child soldier but now works as a deminer— a person who removes land mines.

❷ In 2008, he established an NGO (non-governmental organization) to clear land mines in rural areas. Because of the organization's work, thousands of people have been able to return to land that was once too dangerous to farm.

❸ A documentary was made about his life, and he received several international awards.

Closing Experts estimate there are over three million land mines throughout Cambodia. Aki Ra has used his fame to bring attention to this tragedy.

If I Go There

Like many people, I have always wanted to visit Angkor Wat to see the temple's interesting architecture and to learn about its history. Maybe I will ride a tuk tuk to get there.

Step1 ➡ Choose one country. Research what celebrities come from there.

Step2 ➡ Write more than 100 words using three good points. Use some of the useful expressions, if you like.

Countries
- Burkina Faso
- Burundi
- Cambodia
- Cameroon
- Canada
- Cape Verde

Cambodia

Country

_____

National Flag

Step3 ➡ If I Go There

Country
Chile

Opening The climate in one area of Chile is so arid it created the driest non-polar desert in the world.

Body ① The Atacama Desert has more than 300 days of clear skies annually and no light pollution. This makes it the perfect location for the world's largest ground telescope.

② There is evidence that many parts of this barren landscape have not had any substantial rainfall for hundreds of years.

③ The area is home to the Chinchorro mummies. Predating Egyptian mummies by almost 3,000 years, they are the oldest artificially mummified remains ever found.

Closing Take plenty of water when you visit the Atacama Desert, but do not take your mummy.

If I Go There

Although Chile's deserts are impressive, I like the cold more than the heat, so I would like to visit the glaciers in Patagonia. Some of them are over 60 meters in height. Cool!

Step 1 ▪□ Choose one country. Research what the climate is like.

Step 2 ▪□ Write more than 100 words using three good points.
Use some of the useful expressions, if you like.

Countries
- Central African Republic ※
- Chad
- Chile
- China
- Colombia
- Comoros ※

※Please use "the" before this country name
if you use it in a sentence.

Chile

Country _____

National Flag

Step 3 ▪□ If I Go There

Step 4 ▪□ After writing, share your ideas with your friends.

19

7 Currencies

Country
Costa Rica

Opening If you want to use money with a picture of a shark on it, you have got to go to the Central American country of Costa Rica!

Body

❶ Costa Rican currency is called the colón. It is named after Christopher Columbus whose name is Cristóbal Colón in Spanish.

❷ The notes come in 1,000, 2,000, 5,000, 10,000, 20,000 and 50,000 denominations.

❸ The 2,000 colónes note is vibrant blue showing a coral reef and a bull shark. It is amazing to see.

Closing If you travel to Costa Rica, take a good look at their bank notes. I think you will want to keep some as souvenirs.

If I Go There

Costa Rica is the perfect place for the active traveler. But I would like to take it easy and visit the Sloth Sanctuary to see the slow-moving mammal in its natural habitat.

Step 1 ▪□ Choose one country. Research what currency they use.

Step 2 ▪□ Write more than 100 words using three good points.
Use some of the useful expressions, if you like.

Countries

- Congo ※
- Costa Rica
- Croatia
- Cuba
- Cyprus
- Czech Republic

Costa Rica

※Please use "the" before this country name
if you use it in a sentence.

Country

_____

National Flag

Step 3 ▪□ If I Go There

Step 4 ▪□ After writing, share your ideas with your friends.

21

Desserts

Sample Sentences

Country
Dominican Republic

Opening The number of great desserts in the Dominican Republic is almost too many to count!

Body ❶ Natives might say *dulce de leche Dominicano* (Dominican milk fudge) is their favorite. It is a mixture of sugar and milk and it looks like a creamy, thick sauce.

❷ *Habichuelas con dulce* (sweet beans) is like a smooth pudding. It is a traditional holiday dessert.

❸ *Bizcocho Dominicano* (Dominican sponge cake) is a light and airy cake. What makes it so special is the frosting made from meringue, which is used to make gorgeous designs.

Closing The Dominican Republic is a great destination for anyone with a sweet tooth. Falling in love with their desserts is a piece of cake.

If I Go There

The Cueva de las Maravillas is an enormous cave that is around 100,000 years old. It is full of stalactites and stalagmites and ancient people drew pictographs on the cave walls. I really want to see this place.

Step1 ➞ Choose one country. Research what desserts they eat.

Step2 ➞ Write more than 100 words using three good points.
Use some of the useful expressions, if you like.

Countries

- Democratic People's Republic of Korea (North Korea)
- Democratic Republic of the Congo
- Denmark
- Djibouti
- Dominica
- Dominican Republic ※
- Ecuador

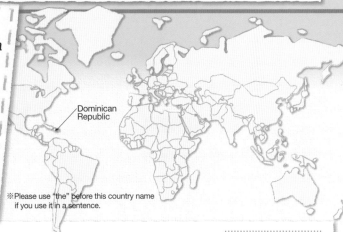

Dominican Republic

※Please use "the" before this country name if you use it in a sentence.

Country _____

National Flag

Step3 ➞ If I Go There

Step4 ➞ After writing, share your ideas with your friends.

9 Drinks

Sample Sentences

Country
Egypt

Opening It is well known that the ancient pharaohs enjoyed beer around 3,000 BC, but here are three soft drinks that Egyptians enjoy today.

Body ❶ *Qasab*, which is basically sugarcane juice, is a delicious Egyptian beverage served chilled on hot summer days.

❷ *Karkade*—a type of iced tea—was believed to be popular among the ancient pharaohs thousands of years ago and is enjoyed by adults today.

❸ *Fayrouz* is a blend of malt, fruit and sparkling water. It comes in a variety of flavors such as apple, peach and pineapple. Egyptian kids are crazy about this drink!

Closing I think sipping a cold Egyptian drink while sitting next to the pyramids would be fun.

If I Go There

It has always been a dream of mine to visit the pyramids of Giza! I have seen pictures of people riding camels around those ancient structures. I want to do that, too!

Step 1 ᗍ Choose one country. Research what drinks you can have.

Step 2 ᗍ Write more than 100 words using three good points.
Use some of the useful expressions, if you like.

Countries

- **Egypt**
- El Salvador
- Equatorial Guinea
- Eritrea
- Estonia
- Eswatini
- Ethiopia

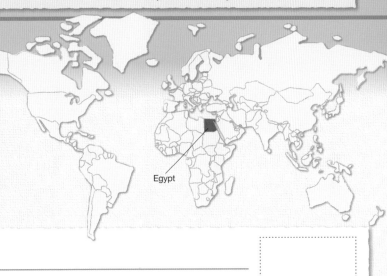

Egypt

Country _____

National Flag

_____

_____

_____

_____

_____

_____

_____

_____

 Step 3 ᗍ If I Go There

_____

_____

_____

_____

Step 4 ᗍ After writing, share your ideas with your friends.

10 Education

Country
Georgia

Tbilisi Classical Gymnasium

Opening To some extent, education in Georgia is similar to that in Japan, but needless to say, there are also some big differences.

Body ❶ Many of the same subjects are taught in both countries. For example, Georgian and Japanese students study math, science, and English.

❷ In contrast, Japanese students go to school well over 200 days a year while Georgian students go about 170.

❸ That is mainly because the summer holiday in Georgia is so much longer than in Japan. Georgian students get about three months for vacation, but Japanese students only get about 40 days.

Closing There are positives and negatives in all educational systems. The important thing is for students to try to become the best they can be.

If I Go There

Walking around the Old Town area of Georgia's capital sounds very interesting. But I would really like to visit the province of Svaneti to see the old watchtowers built in the Middle Ages.

Step 1 ▭ Choose one country. Research what the education system is like.

Step 2 ▭ Write more than 100 words using three good points. Use some of the useful expressions, if you like.

Countries

- Federated States of Micronesia (Micronesia)
- Fiji
- Finland
- France
- Gabon
- Georgia
- Germany

Georgia

Country _____

National Flag

....

....

....

....

....

....

....

....

Step 3 ▭ If I Go There

....

....

....

....

Step 4 ▭ After writing, share your ideas with your friends.

27

11 Fashion

Country
Ghana

Opening It is fascinating to learn how Ghana's beautiful traditional clothing can represent so many things.

Body
1. Perhaps the most beautiful of the country's traditional garments is kente cloth.
2. There are more than 300 different patterns. What is more, each one has a unique meaning.
3. Colors have symbolic meanings, too. For example, at funerals, Ghanaians sometimes wear red, black and white. Red represents death and black signifies mourning. White is worn to celebrate the life of someone who lived past 80.

Closing Some companies have started a policy encouraging their employees to wear traditional clothes to work on Fridays. The policy is called "Thank Ghana it's Friday."

If I Go There

I love elephants, so I would like to visit the Mole National Park. It is Ghana's largest wildlife refuge where more than 600 elephants roam freely. Maybe I could see some baby elephants there.

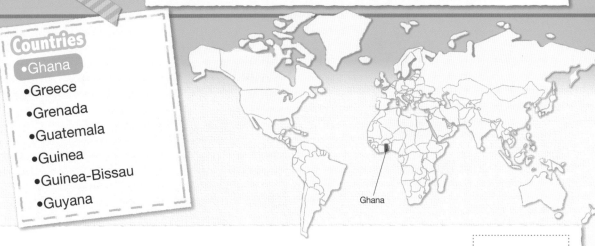

Step1 ▫ Choose one country. Research what fashions people wear.

Step2 ▫ Write more than 100 words using three good points.
Use some of the useful expressions, if you like.

Countries
- Ghana
- Greece
- Grenada
- Guatemala
- Guinea
- Guinea-Bissau
- Guyana

Ghana

Country

National Flag

Step3 ▫ If I Go There

Step4 ▫ After writing, share your ideas with your friends.

12 Festivals

Country
India

Opening The number of interesting Indian festivals and celebrations is mind blowing.

Body ❶ Probably the most popular among Indian families is the Diwali Festival—the Festival of Lights.

❷ In the very famous Dussehra Festival, huge figures of demon king Ravana are burned. It also marks the end of the Durga Puja, and beautiful clay statues of the Goddess Durga are immersed in rivers or the ocean.

❸ The Holi Festival is world famous! At the event, people throw brightly colored powder and water at each other and get completely covered in colors.

Closing Thousands of tourists travel to India each year to take part in festival fun! Would you like to visit and enjoy the great traditions of India?

If I Go There

I have always wanted to see the Festival of Colors. It really looks fun! I am sure I would be able to feel the passion of the Indian people for their festivals.

Step1 ▭ Choose one country. Research what festivals they have.

Step2 ▭ Write more than 100 words using three good points.
Use some of the useful expressions, if you like.

Countries
- Haiti
- Honduras
- Hungary
- Iceland
- India
- Indonesia

India

Country

_____

National Flag

Step3 ▭ If I Go There

Country
Italy

Opening It is so easy to spot Italian restaurants wherever you go in the world. Why? Because owners make it a rule to always have Italian flags displayed.

Body

❶ The colors of the Italian flag are green, white and red.

❷ Green signifies the plains and hills of Italy, white represents the snowy Alps, and red stands for the blood spilled in war.

❸ The famous margherita pizza is comprised of green basil, white cheese and red tomatoes, which are the same colors as the flag.

Closing It is not hard to imagine that every time you look at the Italian flag, you will think of a margherita pizza. And of course, every time you eat a margherita pizza, you will think of the Italian flag.

 If I Go There

I have always hoped to visit the many popular tourist spots in Rome, such as the Colosseum and the Pantheon. I would also like to stroll around the famous Spanish Steps.

Step1 ☞ Choose one country. Research what flag they use.

Step2 ☞ Write more than 100 words using three good points.
Use some of the useful expressions, if you like.

Countries
- Iraq
- Ireland
- Islamic Republic of Iran (Iran)
- Israel
- Italy
- Ivory Coast
- Jamaica

Italy

Country

National Flag

Step3 ☞ If I Go There

Step4 ☞ After writing, share your ideas with your friends.

33

14 Flowers

Country
Jordan

Opening A national flower can be an accurate reflection of a country's character. This is especially true for the intriguing Middle Eastern nation of Jordan.

Body ❶ The county's national flower is the exquisitely beautiful black iris.

❷ The petals are actually very dark purple but appear black. The blackish coloring is why the flower got its name. It can grow about 30 centimeters tall during spring and can be seen across the country.

❸ Some people call the black iris "the queen of wild flowers." It is Jordan's inspirational symbol of growth, renewal and change for the nation and its citizens.

Closing Like the people of Jordan, the black iris has a reputation for toughness and perseverance.

If I Go There

I want to visit the ancient city of Petra which is famous for its beautiful stone carvings. The entrance is through a long, narrow canyon called the Siq. This place really looks fantastic!

Step 1 ▪□ Choose one country. Research what flowers grow.

Step 2 ▪□ Write more than 100 words using three good points.
Use some of the useful expressions, if you like.

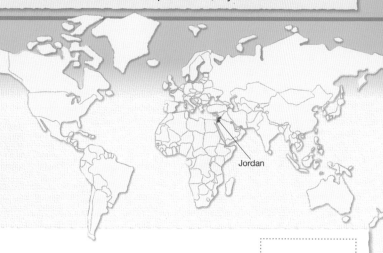

Countries
- Japan
- Jordan
- Kazakhstan
- Kenya
- Kiribati
- Kuwait
- Kyrgyzstan

Jordan

Country _____

....

National Flag

....

....

....

....

....

....

Step 3 ▪□ If I Go There

....

....

....

Step 4 ▪□ After writing, share your ideas with your friends.

35

15 *History*

Country
Liechtenstein

Opening Liechtenstein is a peaceful European microstate with an area of only 160 square kilometers—that is as small as Shodo Island in Japan. Although it is tiny, the country has an interesting history.

Body ❶ The nation gained independence in 1866 and is named after the Liechtenstein family.

❷ In 1868, the country disbanded its army of about 80 men and declared its neutrality. The country was neutral during both World Wars.

❸ Incredibly, Liechtenstein was the last European nation to give women the right to vote. Women voted in national elections for the first time in 1984.

Closing Naturally, people tend to think small countries could be boring, but Liechtenstein is a beautiful place with a long history.

If I Go There

I want to visit castles in Liechtenstein. In particular, I would like to see the Gutenberg Castle, which was built in the Middle Ages but is still in wonderful condition.

Step1 Choose one country. Research what the history is.

Step2 Write more than 100 words using three good points.
Use some of the useful expressions, if you like.

Countries

- Lao People's Democratic Republic (Laos)
- Latvia
- Lebanon
- Lesotho
- Liberia
- Libya
- Liechtenstein

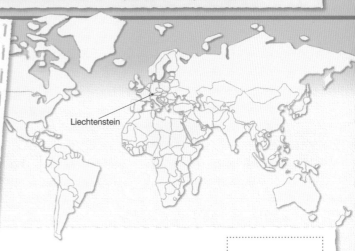

Liechtenstein

Country _____

National Flag

 Step3 If I Go There

Country
Madagascar

Opening Every country has its own strange and frightening stories. Are you brave enough to read about the horror stories of Madagascar?

Body

❶ Angatras are ghosts that haunt graves and bring misfortune to those who anger them.

❷ "Turning of the Bones" is a Malagasy custom in which families dance and celebrate with the bones of their deceased relatives. Spooky!

❸ Kalanoros are ape-like UMAs (Unidentified Mysterious Animals) believed to live deep inside the rainforests of Madagascar. They are about 60 centimeters tall with hooked fingers and long fingernails. Similar to kappa, they are said to love water.

Closing Be careful when traveling to Madagascar. You do not want to see any ghosts or monsters while you are there, do you?

If I Go There

I would like to see the world's largest stone forest in the Tsingy de Bemaraha National Park. I want to walk across a suspension bridge over a canyon of sharp, jagged rocks. Scary!

Step 1 ◾ Choose one country. Research what horror stories they have.

Step 2 ◾ Write more than 100 words using three good points.
Use some of the useful expressions, if you like.

Countries
- Lithuania
- Luxembourg
- Madagascar
- Malawi
- Malaysia
- Maldives

Madagascar

Country

National Flag

Step 3 ◾ If I Go There

Step 4 ◾ After writing, share your ideas with your friends.

17 *Houses*

Country
Mexico

Opening Under the blazing skies of Mexico you will find beautiful houses of various and distinctive designs.

Body

1. Historically, traditional Mexican adobe houses were made from sundried bricks to insulate them from the hot sun. Modern Mexican houses feature stone or stucco walls with tiled roofs.

2. The ancient Aztecs often used adobe bricks to construct houses throughout their empire.

3. Adobe is a type of mud brick and is not always painted. The exteriors of adobe homes can be the color of the desert sand and clay used to make them, such as light orange. The interiors are often vibrantly colored.

Closing Mexicans believe bright colors reflect a warm and welcoming home. As the saying goes, *"Mi casa es tu casa."* — "My home is your home."

 If I Go There

The Pyramid of the Sun is the third largest pyramid in the world. Surprisingly, tourists are allowed to climb to the top and take photos. I would love to do that!

Step 1 Choose one country. Research what kind of houses they live in.

Step 2 Write more than 100 words using three good points.
Use some of the useful expressions, if you like.

Countries
- Mali
- Malta
- Marshall Islands
- Mauritania
- Mauritius
- Mexico

Mexico

Country _____

National Flag

Step 3 If I Go There

Step 4 After writing, share your ideas with your friends.

41

18 *Landscapes*

Country
Mongolia

Opening The image many people have of Mongolia is of nomads wearing traditional costumes, riding horses in a vast open landscape.

Body

❶ The Mongolian sky is big and blue during the day and full of stars at night. Huge open grasslands cover parts of the country.

❷ The Gobi Desert offers a different kind of scenery and was the stomping grounds of many kinds of dinosaurs millions of years ago. Can you imagine that?

❸ When you stand in the middle of the Gobi, you can enjoy the 360-degree panorama of nothing on the horizon.

Closing In order to truly appreciate the landscape of Mongolia, you should stay in a ger, a traditional Mongolian tent house.

If I Go There

I would like to stay in a ger to get a true feeling of how Mongolians live. Maybe I can meet a famous Mongolian sumo wrestler.

Step1 ◻ Choose one country. Research what landscapes you can see.

Step2 ◻ Write more than 100 words using three good points. Use some of the useful expressions, if you like.

Countries

- Monaco
- Mongolia
- Montenegro
- Morocco
- Mozambique
- Myanmar

Mongolia

Country _____

National Flag

Step3 ◻ If I Go There

Step4 ◻ After writing, share your ideas with your friends.

19 Languages

Sample Sentences

Country

Namibia

Opening *"Halo! Ongaipi?"* translates to "Hello! How are you?" from Oshiwambo—the most widely spoken language in the African nation of Namibia.

Body

❶ The Oshiwambo alphabet is similar to the English alphabet, but without the letters c, q and x.

❷ The country's official language is English, but fewer than 10 percent of Namibians speak it as their first language. As a matter of fact, the Oshiwambo dialect (a native language of the country) is spoken by almost half of the population of 2.5 million.

❸ Amazingly, about 30 dialects are used throughout Namibia—around 22 of them are indigenous.

Closing Why not visit Namibia and try to learn one more language? *"Kala po nawa."*—"Goodbye."

If I Go There

Tourists are allowed to climb to the top of Namibia's perfectly shaped 80-meter-tall Dune 45. Although it may look easy, climbing up hot sand is HARD! But I want to try!

Step1 ◗ Choose one country. Research what languages they use.

Step2 ◗ Write more than 100 words using three good points.
Use some of the useful expressions, if you like.

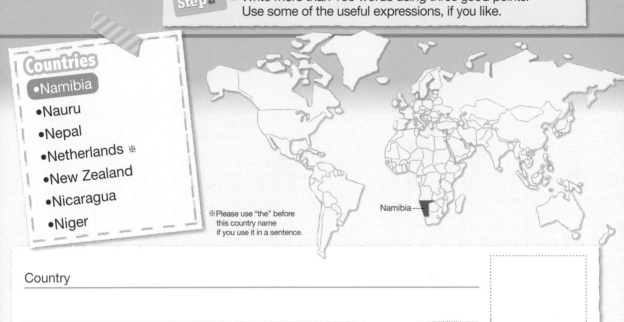

Countries
- Namibia
- Nauru
- Nepal
- Netherlands ※
- New Zealand
- Nicaragua
- Niger

※Please use "the" before this country name if you use it in a sentence.

Namibia

Country _____

National Flag

Step3 ◗ If I Go There

Step4 ◗ After writing, share your ideas with your friends.

20 Leisure

Country
Norway

Opening Norwegians love their leisure time, so it is not surprising Norway has so many amusement parks, aquariums and zoos!

Body
1. The most visited theme park is Tusenfryd. It has many rides and attractions. There are also a variety of places nearby for more family recreation.
2. Polar Park is a spacious zoo. It is the perfect place to see predators of the Arctic.
3. Atlantic Sea Park is one of the largest aquariums in the world. Visitors can learn about Norwegian coastal marine life.

Closing With so many nice places to go plus a generous social welfare system, Norway often ranks number one in the world for being the best country to live in!

If I Go There

I would like to take the Dovre Railway that runs from Oslo to Trondheim. It travels through some of Norway's best national parks, mountains and valleys. That is a nice way to see nature!

Step 1 ➜ Choose one country. Research what leisure activities you can do.

Step 2 ➜ Write more than 100 words using three good points.
Use some of the useful expressions, if you like.

Countries

- Nigeria
- North Macedonia
- Norway
- Oman
- Pakistan
- Palau
- Panama

Norway

Country _____

National Flag

Step 3 ➜ If I Go There

Step 4 ➜ After writing, share your ideas with your friends.

21 Local Food

Country
Poland

Opening Millions of people say *pierogi* is one of the most delicious foods in Europe.

Body
① *Pierogi* is the national dish of Poland. People eat these tasty dumplings at many different occasions all year round.

② They can be filled with almost anything. For instance, foods such as meat, cabbage, and mushrooms are often used. People even make them with strawberries or sweet cheese to eat as a treat or as a dessert.

③ Interestingly, Polish people often cook *pierogi* similarly to how Japanese prepare gyoza by frying them in a pan until they are golden brown. Yum!

Closing If you like gyoza, you are sure to enjoy the great taste of Poland's favorite food!

If I Go There
The Wieliczka Salt Mine is one of the world's oldest salt mines. I want to explore the mining shafts and tunnels and see how people used to produce salt.

Step1 ➡ Choose one country. Research what local food you can eat.

Step2 ➡ Write more than 100 words using three good points.
Use some of the useful expressions, if you like.

Countries
- Papua New Guinea
- Paraguay
- Peru
- Philippines ※
- Plurinational State of Bolivia (Bolivia)
- Poland
- Portugal

Poland

※Please use "the" before this country name if you use it in a sentence.

Country _____

National Flag

Step3 ➡ If I Go There

Step4 ➡ After writing, share your ideas with your friends.

22 Markets

Country
South Korea

Opening A visit to a large market in South Korea is a must.

Body ❶ The Kwangjang Market was established in 1905 and it was Korea's first permanent market that was open every day of the week.

❷ It is located at the eastern end of the historic area of Jongno and has more than 5,000 stalls.

❸ It is mainly a fabric and textile market. People can buy a wide range of woven and knitted goods there. In addition to that, it is also famous for delicious street food such as *bibimbap* (mixed rice), *kimbap* (Korean rolled sushi), and so on.

Closing The bustling atmosphere adds to the excitement of a visit. The market can get very cold in winter. So, if you visit then, you should bundle up!

If I Go There

The Bulguksa Temple and grounds is a major historic site in South Korea. It is home to many national treasures and it is a must-see destination when visiting the country.

Step 1 ◄■ Choose one country. Research what markets you can visit.

Step 2 ◄■ Write more than 100 words using three good points.
Use some of the useful expressions, if you like.

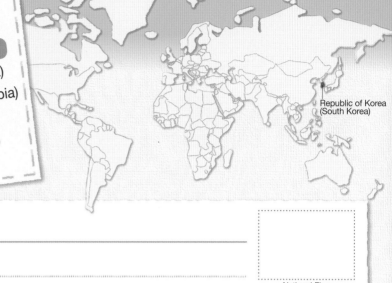

Republic of Korea
(South Korea)

Countries

- Qatar
- Republic of Korea (South Korea)
- Republic of Moldova (Moldova)
- Republic of the Gambia (Gambia)
- Romania
- Russian Federation (Russia)
- Rwanda

Country _____

National Flag

 Step 3 ◄■ If I Go There

Step 4 ◄■ After writing, share your ideas with your friends.

51

23 Myths

Country
Samoa

Opening Like many other indigenous people of the Pacific Islands, ancient Samoans had no written history. Because of this, their storytellers orally passed on ancestral history, myths and legends for generations.

Body

❶ One of their best-known myths is called *Sina and the Eel*.

❷ It is a story about the origin of the coconut tree.

❸ In the tale, an old king turns himself into an eel to travel to Samoa to see the beautiful Sina. When the eel dies, Sina plants the eel's head, creating the first coconut tree.

Closing Ancient people often used mythology to interpret events. Samoan myths are full of exciting, fun and interesting stories explaining the world around us.

If I Go There

I want to visit some of Samoa's picturesque waterfalls. I especially want to see the Togitogiga Waterfall, where ancient Samoan warriors swam underneath the falls. Maybe I will take a swim like a warrior.

Step1 Choose one country. Research what myths they have.

Step2 Write more than 100 words using three good points.
Use some of the useful expressions, if you like.

Countries

- Saint Kitts and Nevis
- Saint Lucia
- Saint Vincent and the Grenadines
- Samoa
- San Marino
- Sao Tome and Principe
- Saudi Arabia

Samoa

Country _____

National Flag

Step3 If I Go There

Step4 After writing, share your ideas with your friends.

53

24 National Parks

Country
Singapore

Opening Singapore, famous for ultra-modern buildings and luxurious shopping, is also known as "the Garden City" where greenery can be found almost everywhere you go.

Body
1. The country has over 350 well-maintained parks and four nature reserves.
2. The Singapore Botanic Gardens is the nation's most famous park and has UNESCO World Heritage status. It has many themed gardens, but its most popular attraction is the National Orchid Garden with over 3,000 different varieties of orchids.
3. When Singaporeans get sick of city life, many head for the hiking trails in the Bukit Timah Nature Reserve, home to 40 percent of Singapore's flora and fauna.

Closing The towering buildings of Singapore cannot overshadow the beautiful parks this Asian gem has to offer.

If I Go There

Singapore is a food lover's paradise, so I really want to visit their many food courts. You can eat delicious local and international dishes at cheap prices at any one of them.

Step 1 Choose one country. Research what national parks you can visit.

Step 2 Write more than 100 words using three good points.
Use some of the useful expressions, if you like.

Countries
- Senegal
- Serbia
- Seychelles ※
- Sierra Leone
- Singapore
- Slovakia

※Please use "the" before this country name
if you use it in a sentence.

Singapore

Country

National Flag

Step 3 If I Go There

Step 4 After writing, share your ideas with your friends.

25 Holidays

Sample Sentences

Country
South Africa

Opening South Africa shows how a country can take a tragic history and create national holidays that celebrate hope for the future.

Body ❶ Freedom Day on April 27th commemorates the first democratic elections held in South Africa in 1994.

❷ Heritage Day on September 24th celebrates South Africa's diverse cultural legacy with the goal of achieving a more cohesive nation.

❸ Day of Reconciliation started in 1995 to help heal the damage caused by years of *Apartheid*, and to promote and improve national unity. It is held on December 16th.

Closing National holidays can do much more than just memorialize historic events. They can help bring diverse people together in celebration to create a more unified nation.

If I Go There

There are many interesting hiking trails in South Africa.
Some are very challenging and others are fairly easy.
I would like to go on the not-so-difficult Dolphin Hiking Trail to see the beauty of the country.

Step1 ⊷ Choose one country. Research what holidays you can take.

Step2 ⊷ Write more than 100 words using three good points.
Use some of the useful expressions, if you like.

Countries
- Slovenia
- Solomon Islands
- Somalia
- South Africa
- South Sudan
- Spain

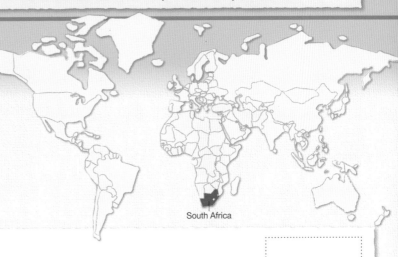

South Africa

Country
_____

National Flag

 Step3 ⊷ If I Go There

Step4 ⊷ After writing, share your ideas with your friends.

26 Rivers

Sample Sentences

Country
Switzerland

Opening People often think of the Alps when picturing the geography of Switzerland, but the country also has a large number of rivers.

Body
1 The Aare River is about 295 kilometers long and runs entirely within the country.
2 Its gentle current along the Old Town area of the nation's capital makes it suitable for traveling downstream on an inflated tube. This popular activity is called tubing, and it is a fun way to cool down in summer.
3 Landmarks such as clock towers, cathedrals and traditional Swiss buildings make for spectacular views from the river.

Closing Floating down the Aare River on a hot summer afternoon would make an unforgettable memory.

If I Go There

Switzerland is famous for its great skiing, but I cannot ski. That is okay because I can spend more time eating delicious Swiss chocolate. I think I will go on a chocolate tour. Yum!

Step1 ▪ Choose one country. Research what rivers you can see.

Step2 ▪ Write more than 100 words using three good points.
Use some of the useful expressions, if you like.

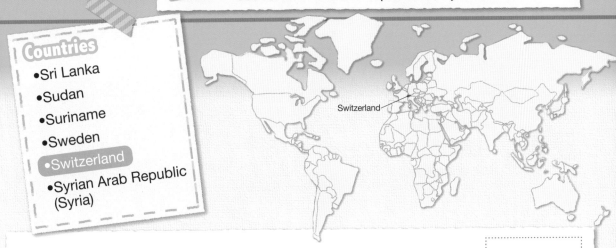

Countries
- Sri Lanka
- Sudan
- Suriname
- Sweden
- Switzerland
- Syrian Arab Republic (Syria)

Switzerland

Country _____

National Flag

Step3 ▪ If I Go There

Step4 ▪ After writing, share your ideas with your friends.

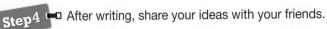

27 Souvenirs

Country
Thailand

Opening Thailand is a fun travel destination, but what are some great Thai souvenirs that are guaranteed to please?

Body ❶ Durian chips are a salty treat and make an awesome gift, but maybe your friends would like something even more unusual—such as a large quantity of fried insects! Yum!

❷ Coconut oil is a very popular product for health, and since many people say Thailand is "the motherland of coconuts," it would also make a super gift for someone special.

❸ Elephants are the symbol of Thailand and are said to be lucky. Any gift featuring elephants will bring good fortune.

Closing Souvenirs from the Land of Smiles are sure to make anyone grin.

If I Go There

The spectacular Grand Palace in Bangkok is definitely something I want to see. It was home to the Thai Royal Family for almost 145 years. The architecture is breathtaking!

Step 1 Choose one country. Research what souvenirs you can buy.

Step 2 Write more than 100 words using three good points.
Use some of the useful expressions, if you like.

Countries
- Tajikistan
- Thailand
- Timor-Leste
- Togo
- Tonga
- Trinidad and Tobago

Thailand

Country

National Flag

Step 3 If I Go There

Step 4 After writing, share your ideas with your friends.

61

28 Sports

Country
Turkey

Opening Turks are known to be passionate and strong. In sports, they clearly show these attributes.

Body ❶ Soccer is by far the most popular spectator sport in Turkey. The Turkish Super League has hired many top players from around the world, including Japanese players.

❷ The national sport is Turkish oil wrestling. Competitors put olive oil on their bodies to make fighting more difficult.

❸ In international competitions, many medals go to Turks in such sports as karate, Taekwondo and kickboxing.

Closing Turks are the tough descendants of the Turkish Empire (Ottoman Empire), and they bring that toughness to the sports they play.

If I Go There

I have always wanted to visit the underground city of Derinkuyu. Its many levels housed thousands of people along with livestock and other necessities in times of war and other emergencies. It must be incredible to see.

Step 1 ⊸ Choose one country. Research what sports you can do.

Step 2 ⊸ Write more than 100 words using three good points.
Use some of the useful expressions, if you like.

Countries
- Tunisia
- Turkey
- Turkmenistan
- Tuvalu
- Uganda
- Ukraine

Turkey

Country _____

National Flag

Step 3 ⊸ If I Go There

Step 4 ⊸ After writing, share your ideas with your friends.

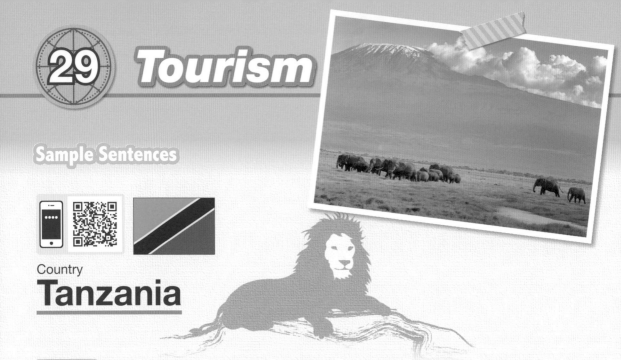

Sample Sentences

Country
Tanzania

Opening Tanzania is the perfect place for people who dream of seeing the magnificent sights of Africa!

Body ❶ You can witness the world's largest migration of animals at the Serengeti National Park.

❷ Mt. Kilimanjaro is the continent's highest peak and more than 2,000 meters higher than Mt. Fuji. A hike up to the top is an amazing challenge.

❸ Mafia Island only gets a few thousand visitors a year, but it is one of the best places in Africa to see interesting marine life including whale sharks. You can also dive and snorkel in this isolated, secret spot.

Closing There is no way you can get bored in Africa's tourist paradise.

If I Go There

I want to go on a safari in the Serengeti. You can see so many animals there including the big cats and their prey. It would be the experience of a lifetime.

Step 1 ▭ Choose one country. Research what tourism activities they have.

Step 2 ▭ Write more than 100 words using three good points. Use some of the useful expressions, if you like.

Countries

- United Arab Emirates (UAE) ※
- United Kingdom of Great Britain and Northern Ireland (UK) ※
- United Republic of Tanzania (Tanzania)
- United States of America (USA) ※
- Uruguay
- Uzbekistan

※Please use "the" before this country name if you use it in a sentence.

United Republic of Tanzania (Tanzania)

Country _____

National Flag

_____

_____

_____

_____

_____

_____

_____

Step 3 ▭ If I Go There

_____

_____

_____

_____

Step 4 ▭ After writing, share your ideas with your friends.

30 World Famous

Sample Sentences

Country
Zimbabwe

Opening As you might already know, the largest waterfall in the world is Victoria Falls in Africa. But which country is it in?

Body
1. In fact, Victoria Falls is on the border of Zimbabwe and Zambia.
2. During the rainy season, mist from the falls rises up to around 800 meters and can be seen from 50 kilometers away.
3. Of course it depends on the weather, but many people think the best time to see the falls is from June to August. During these months, you can usually get an excellent view of the water crashing to the bottom.

Closing The scale of this natural wonder is beyond imagination. It would be great to see Victoria Falls!

If I Go There

Do I dare take a swim in the Devil's Pool? It is nature's ultimate infinity pool high above Victoria Falls with a 100-meter drop to the bottom. It sounds so scary—but I will do it!

Step 1 Choose one country. Research what world famous people or things they have.

Step 2 Write more than 100 words using three good points. Use some of the useful expressions, if you like.

Countries
- Vanuatu
- Viet Nam
- Yemen
- Zambia
- Zimbabwe

Zimbabwe

Country _____

National Flag

Step 3 If I Go There

Step 4 After writing, share your ideas with your friends.

67

Series 1:TAGAKI ⑩ ~ ㊿

Teach Yourself

- Use sample sentences to write good English
- Think and write, then share your ideas
- Develop your interest with 30 x 5 textbooks=150 global topics
- Learn to write with structure: catchy sentences, facts, opinions, and punch lines
- Be independent learners. Evaluate yourself

TAGAKI ⑩
I can do it! Write and check it by yourself
Learn to write three short sentences about 30 daily topics

TAGAKI ⑳
Choose your position: agree or disagree
Learn to clearly express your feelings

TAGAKI ㉚
Pretend to be a third person and write
Learn to write with structure: catchy sentences, facts, opinions, and punch lines

TAGAKI ㊵
Write two original sentences
Learn to write about global topics

TAGAKI ㊿
Research a topic for additional facts and write about them
State your opinion and make your own punch lines

TAGAKI Advanced 2 Around the World

First Published 2020
Fourth Published 2021
Writers: David Staggs, Yoko Matsuka
Contributors: Miyuki Kasuya, Rieko Kondo
English Proofreader: Glenn McDougall
Production: EDIT Co., Ltd.
Illustrators: Taira Nakayama, Yumi Inaba
Designer: Taira Nakayama
DTP Designer: Taira Design
Photos: Cambodia Mines-remove Campaign, Embassy of Namibia, imagenavi, istock, PIXTA, Shutterstock, 123RF
Record Producer: JAILHOUSE MUSIC Inc.
Narrators: Carolyn Miller, Howard Colefield, Peter von Gomm, Rumiko Varnes
Printer: Shinano Co., Ltd.
Special thanks to Chisato Mattox, Hiroko Sadano, Hiromi Sasaki, Kazuko Okazaki, Mie Nonaka, Mika Suzuki, Yuri Akamatsu, Mio, Riku, Taichi, Mitsuru Izumi, Asociación de la Amistad Dominico-Japonesa, Embassy of Georgia, Embassy of India, Embassy of Madagascar, Office of Agricultural Affairs-Royal Thai Embassy, The National Museum of Nature and Science-Tsukuba Research Departments, Tokyo University of Marine Science and Technology, University of Namibia
Publisher: mpi Matsuka Phonics inc.
        2nd Koda Bldg 2F 2-16-2 Yoyogi,
        Shibuya-ku, Tokyo 151-0053 Japan
        fax:03-5302-1652
        URL: https://www.mpi-j.co.jp
ISBN 978-4-89643-777-5
Printed in Japan

Download the audio files from the QR code or web page.
https://www.mpi-j.co.jp/contents/shop/mpi/contents/digital/tagaki_advanced_02.html